This book belongs to

_____

Welcome to my illustrated world of Night Gardens!

Relax and explore a world of engaging pen–and–ink illustrations, all waiting to be brought to life through color. For artists, gardeners, and fantasy lovers of all ages.

The designs are filled with intricate and whimsical pictures to satisfy all skill levels. If you like exploring twilight forests, quiet crafts, and unique ways to unwind, then take an evening amble through these charming pages.

The day has ended, your dreams are waiting…

See more at rjhampson.com

🅕 🅞 russelljamesart

Published by Hop Skip Jump
PO Box 1324 Buderim Queensland Australia 4556

First published 2022.
Copyright © 2023 R. J. Hampson.

ISBN: 978-1-922472-17-5

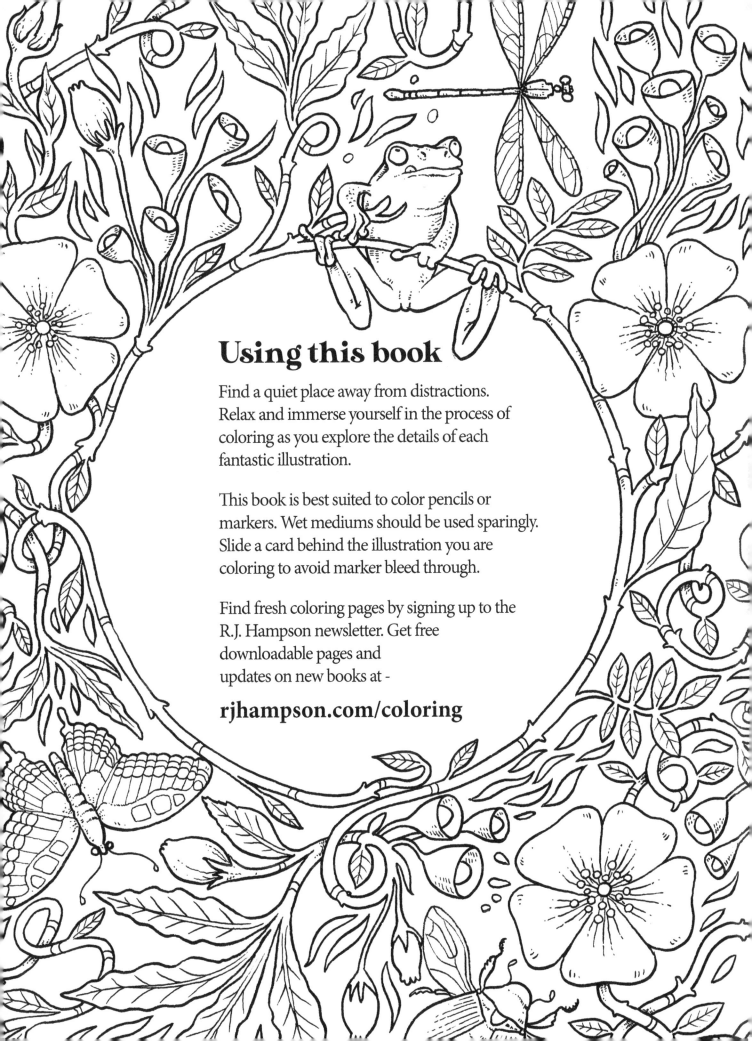

Using this book

Find a quiet place away from distractions. Relax and immerse yourself in the process of coloring as you explore the details of each fantastic illustration.

This book is best suited to color pencils or markers. Wet mediums should be used sparingly. Slide a card behind the illustration you are coloring to avoid marker bleed through.

Find fresh coloring pages by signing up to the R.J. Hampson newsletter. Get free downloadable pages and updates on new books at -

rjhampson.com/coloring

HOMEWARD BOUND

FAWN IN BRAMBLES

FOREST CABIN

HANGING GARDENS

DRAGON GATE

MR FOGHERTY BEGINS A LONG JOURNEY

ELVEN HOME

WILD ROSE

ROSE CASTLE

OUT OF EDEN

GRASSLANDS

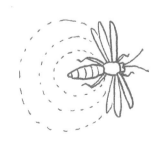

FIREFLY

BUTTERFLY

NOCTURNE

CHERRY BLOSSOMS

CUCKOO CLOCK

JUNGLE NIGHTS

ROYAL GARDENS

RAPUNZEL

TWILIGHT IN THE MAGNOLIA TREE

FROGS

LARRY VS THE MONSTER FLOWERS

THE GLOAMING

TINY WINDMILL

TROUBLE

Need more coloring treats?

Find new coloring pages by signing up to Russell's newsletter.
Get free downloadable pages and updates on new books at -
rjhampson.com/coloring

Thanks for choosing this coloring book.
If you enjoyed it, please consider leaving a review.
It will help to let more people in on the experience
plus you'd certainly make this illustrator very happy!

Published books in this series

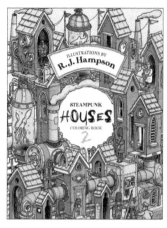

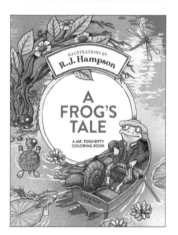

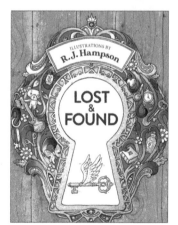

See flip-throughs and new releases at **rjhampson.com**

Printed in the USA
CPSIA information can be obtained
at www.ICGtesting.com
LVHW061753250923
759185LV00014B/809